MASTER YOUR SPELLING

G. C. Davies, S. M. Dillon and T. D. Dillon

Illustrated by G. C. Davies

Basil Blackwell

How to use this book

1. Look hard at the words in the first box on the page.
2. Copy out the first word neatly in large letters.
3. Trace over the letters with your finger.
4. Say the word slowly and spell it aloud.
5. Close your eyes. Make a picture of the word in your mind.
6. 'Write' the word on the table with your finger.
7. Cover the word and really write it.
8. If it is correct, write it in your word book. If it is not, learn it again until you know it. *Then* write it in your word book.
9. Do this for each word in each box or in each puzzle.
10. The 'Mini Revision' exercises are for extra practice.
11. Your teacher should mark the five tests in the book.

First published 1983   Reprinted 1984
Published by Basil Blackwell
108 Cowley Road
Oxford OX4 1JF
Typeset in Linotron Century Schoolbook by Oxford Publishing Services, Oxford
Printed in Great Britain
ISBN 0 631 91100 6

resigned design sign
designed signed ensign

Complete these sentences. Use the words in the box.

1 The headmaster s _ _ _ _ _ every child's report.
2 The traffic s _ _ _ warned of the junction ahead.
3 The wallpaper had a pretty d _ _ _ _ _ on it.
4 Ford Motors have d _ _ _ _ _ _ _ a new sports car.
5 Mr Jones r _ _ _ _ _ _ _ from his job as manager.
6 The Royal Navy's flag is the white e _ _ _ _ _.

chocolate scraped bacon
companion stomach behaviour
champion frightened

Complete these sentences. Use the words in the box.

1 Christine had eggs and b _ _ _ _ for breakfast.
2 Dad s _ _ _ _ _ _ the side of the car on the wall.
3 Do you prefer milk c _ _ _ _ _ _ _ _ to plain?
4 Many people are f _ _ _ _ _ _ _ _ _ of thunderstorms.
5 The poodle is the c _ _ _ _ _ _ _ dog of the show.
6 Your b _ _ _ _ _ _ _ _ is bad and must improve.
7 Old Ben's dog has been his c _ _ _ _ _ _ _ _ for years.
8 Sally had an awful pain in her s _ _ _ _ _ _.

| aeroplane   aerial   aerodrome
aerosol   aeronautics   aerobatics | |

Complete these sentences. Use the words in the box.

1 I'm not travelling in that a _ _ _ p _ _ _ _.
2 Our television a _ _ _ _ _ was damaged in the storm.
3 Bob will study a _ _ _ n _ _ _ _ _ _ at flying school.
4 Not every a _ _ _ d _ _ _ _ has a concrete runway.
5 Steve sprayed his cycle with an a _ _ _ s _ _ can.
6 We watched the aircraft doing _ _ _ _ b _ _ _ _ _ overhead.

| fulfil   skilful   wilful   spiteful
awful   tearful   powerful   disgraceful | |

Complete these sentences. Use the words in the box.

1 The factory was unable to f _ _ _ _ _ all its orders.
2 Smith was charged with w _ _ _ _ _ damage to the car.
3 Sarah was t _ _ _ _ _ _ on her first day at school.
4 The racing car had a p _ _ _ _ _ _ _ engine.
5 Eva must control that a _ _ _ _ temper of hers.
6 It was s _ _ _ _ _ _ _ to tell a lie about me.
7 What a d _ _ _ _ _ _ _ _ _ _ mess the boys have made.
8 David is the most s _ _ _ _ _ _ player in the team.

| preparation observation operation population taxation declaration education | tion |

Complete these sentences. Use the words in the box.

1   Scientists need keen powers of o _ _ _ _ _ _ _ _ _ _.

2   The p _ _ _ _ _ _ _ _ of Great Britain is about
     52 millions.

3   Most children finish their e _ _ _ _ _ _ _ _ at sixteen.

4   The Government raises money by t _ _ _ _ _ _ _.

5   Sam had an o _ _ _ _ _ _ _ _ to remove his appendix.

6   The class made hats in p _ _ _ _ _ _ _ _ _ _ for
     the party.

7   A d _ _ _ _ _ _ _ _ _ _ of war is a serious matter.

| action   fraction   friction junction   fiction   function |

Decode the answers to the clues using this key.

a = Ֆ   f = ⧖   i = ∞   j = <   n = φ

r = ⌐   u = ⊿   ction = ⋉

The words in the box will help you.

1   Part of a whole

2   Meeting of two roads

3   Not fact

4   Special event

5   Rubbing to make heat

6   Doing something

1	⧖ ⌐ Ֆ ⋉
2	< ⊿ φ ⋉
3	⧖ ∞ ⋉
4	⧖ ⊿ φ ⋉
5	⧖ ⌐ ∞ ⋉
6	Ֆ ⋉

5

> section   collection
> resolution   competition
> condition   companion
> motion   champion

Complete these sentences.
Use the words in the box.

1   Wilfred made a New Year's r _ _ _ _ _ _ _ _ _.
2   Never get off a bus when it is in m _ _ _ _ _.
3   Terry entered the c _ _ _ _ _ _ _ _ _ _ to win a car.
4   The police closed a s _ _ _ _ _ _ of the motorway.
5   Mohammed Ali was a great world c _ _ _ _ _ _ _.
6   John and his c _ _ _ _ _ _ _ _ went on a hike.
7   A c _ _ _ _ _ _ _ _ _ was taken for the children's home.
8   The vintage car was in very good c _ _ _ _ _ _ _ _.

> foundation   organisation   situation
> determination   location   navigation
> information   partition

Complete these sentences. Use the words in the box.

1   My mistake put me in an awkward s _ _ _ _ _ _ _ _.
2   You can get tourist i _ _ _ _ _ _ _ _ _ _ from the kiosk.
3   The f _ _ _ _ _ _ _ _ _ of a house must be very strong.
4   Oxfam is a charitable o _ _ _ _ _ _ _ _ _ _ _.
5   The ship's n _ _ _ _ _ _ _ _ _ system was damaged.
6   Colin showed great d _ _ _ _ _ _ _ _ _ _ _ _ to recover.
7   The aircraft gave the gunners the exact l _ _ _ _ _ _ _.
8   The p _ _ _ _ _ _ _ _ between the rooms was thin.

6

*Complete these words by adding **tion**.*
Look them up in a dictionary if you
do not know what they mean.

tion

1 destruc _ _ _ _   9 extinc _ _ _ _
2 correc _ _ _ _   10 solu _ _ _ _
3 attrac _ _ _ _   11 cau _ _ _ _
4 distinc _ _ _ _   12 posi _ _ _ _
5 connec _ _ _ _   13 examina _ _ _ _
6 direc _ _ _ _   14 rela _ _ _ _
7 evolu _ _ _ _   15 rota _ _ _ _
8 repeti _ _ _ _   16 organisa _ _ _ _

**connection   repetition   correction
extinction   solution   rotation**

Complete the words in the brackets. Use the words
in the box.

1 Will die out, doomed to (ext _ _ _ _ _ _ _)
2 Done over and over again (rep _ _ _ _ _ _ _)
3 Putting something right (cor _ _ _ _ _ _ _)
4 Going round and round (rot _ _ _ _ _)
5 Fixed together, made a ? (con _ _ _ _ _ _ _)
6 The answer to a problem (sol _ _ _ _ _)

Mini Revision

signed wilful information designs
junction foundation preparation
sign competition condition ensign
stomach population chocolate
aerial aeroplane operation powerful

Complete these sentences. Use the words in the box.

1 Food is digested in the s _ _ _ _ _ _.

2 Ian won a camera in the c _ _ _ _ _ _ _ _ _ _.

3 The boxer had a p _ _ _ _ _ _ _ punch.

4 The pop star s _ _ _ _ _ the autograph book.

5 The Spitfire was a World War II a _ _ _ _ _ _ _ _ .

6 Turn right at the road j _ _ _ _ _ _ _.

7 The Queen laid the f _ _ _ _ _ _ _ _ _ stone of the new church.

8 A heart transplant is a serious o _ _ _ _ _ _ _ _.

9 An architect d _ _ _ _ _ _ new buildings.

10 Easter eggs are either plain or milk
   c _ _ _ _ _ _ _ _.

11 Vandals damaged the radio a _ _ _ _ _ on the car.

12 Careful p _ _ _ _ _ _ _ _ _ _ of the soil is needed before planting seeds.

13 A w _ _ _ _ _ child always wants its own way.

14 The c _ _ _ _ _ _ _ _ of the patient improved.

15 A lot of i _ _ _ _ _ _ _ _ _ _ is stored in computers.

16 The flag of the Merchant Navy is the red e _ _ _ _ _.

17 The p _ _ _ _ _ _ _ _ _ of our schools is getting smaller.

18 The traffic s _ _ _ said, 'Beware of deer!'

official   arrest   suppose
corridor   ragged   squabble
happiness   difficult

assorted
double consonants

Complete these sentences. Use the words in the box.

1 This problem is too d _ _ _ _ _ _ _ for me.
2 Rachel's h _ _ _ _ _ _ _ was seen in her smiling face.
3 Colin got an o _ _ _ _ _ _ warning from the referee.
4 Don't _q _ _ _ _ _ _ about who owns the bicycle.
5 I s _ _ _ _ _ _ I will have to do it myself.
6 A policeman's job is to a _ _ _ _ _ criminals.
7 John walked along the c _ _ _ _ _ _ _ to his room.
8 The tramp's clothes were r _ _ _ _ _ and torn.

occupy   accurate   accused
accept   according   acceptable
accelerate   accustomed

Complete these sentences. Use the words in the box.

1 Tony is absent a _ _ _ _ _ _ _ g to the register.
2 It is always difficult to a _ _ _ _ t defeat.
3 Terry gave an _ _ _ u _ _ _ _ description of the man.
4 The vase made a most _ _ _ _ p _ _ _ _ _ present.
5 His eyes soon became _ _ _ _ _ t _ _ _ _ to the darkness.
6 The new chair will o _ _ _ _ _ that corner nicely.
7 Did you see that car a _ _ _ _ _ _ _ _ _ like a rocket?
8 Mrs Sharp _ _ _ _ _ _ d Ian of stealing the watch.

| occurred committee village appalling accommodation appointment possession |  assorted double consonants |

Complete these words by putting the correct pairs of letters into each space. You will need to use some pairs more than once.

cc mm pp ll rr ss tt

1 A place to live   a _ _ o _ _ odation
2 Ownership   po _ _ e _ _ ion
3 Group of people working together   co _ _ i _ _ ee
4 Happened   o _ _ u _ _ ed
5 Awful, dreadful   a _ _ a _ _ ing
6 A very small town   vi _ _ age
7 Arrangement to meet someone   a _ _ ointment

| immediate immense summer commuters correspond irritating irregular immigrants |

Complete these sentences. Use the words in the box.

1 People who come to live in this country are called i _ _ _ g _ _ _ _ _.
2 The sick man needed i _ _ e _ _ _ _ _ help.
3 John had an i _ _ _ t _ _ _ _ _ rash on his hands.
4 The oil tanker was an i _ _ e _ _ _ ship.
5 The bells rang at irr _ _ _ _ _ _ intervals.
6 This has been the hottest s _ _ _ _ _ on record.
7 People who travel to work are co _ _ ut _ _ _.
8 To write to someone is to co _ _ _ _ p _ _ _.

> imagine medicine definite
> desperate opposite machine
> favourite deliberate

ite, ate and **ine**

Complete these sentences.
Use the words in the box.

1 The club has a m＿＿＿＿＿＿ for throwing tennis balls.
2 Stop hesitating and give a d＿＿＿＿＿＿＿ answer.
3 'Up' is the o＿＿＿＿＿＿＿ of 'down'.
4 Just i＿＿＿＿＿＿ how it feels to be eaten bit by bit!
5 Strawberry is my f＿＿＿＿＿＿＿＿ flavour.
6 A d＿＿＿＿＿＿＿＿＿ attempt was made to spoil the show.
7 We made one last d＿＿＿＿＿＿＿＿ attempt at rescue.
8 Take your m＿＿＿＿＿＿＿ and you'll feel better.

> organise disguise capsize
> paralyse recognise
> otherwise analyse

ise, ize and **yse**

Complete these sentences.
Use the words in the box.

1 The scientist was asked to a＿＿＿＿＿＿ the mixture.
2 This boat will c＿＿＿＿＿＿ in a high wind.
3 Would you r＿＿＿＿＿＿＿＿ the thief again?
4 That snake's bite will p＿＿＿＿＿＿＿ any living thing.
5 It was easy to see through Sidney's d＿＿＿＿＿＿＿.
6 Mr Beak offered to o＿＿＿＿＿＿＿ the concert.
7 Go now, o＿＿＿＿＿＿＿＿ you'll miss the bus.

Test Yourself 1

pages 3 to 11

Complete these sentences. Each dash stands for a letter.

1   The policemen had to a_ _ _ _ _ the protesters.

2   The accident o_ _ _ _ _ _ _ at the roundabout.

3   Many i_ _ _ _ _ _ _ _ _ came from India in the 1950s.

4   The p_ _ _ _ _ _ _ _ between the two rooms fell down.

5   The ghost pointed in Scrooge's d_ _ _ _ _ _ _ _ _.

6   I want two rashers of b_ _ _ _ and an egg, please.

7   Jones was a_ _ _ _ _ _ of murdering his uncle.

8   He is too f_ _ _ _ _ _ _ _ _ to go to the dentist.

9   The a_ _ _ _ _ _ _ _ made a crash landing.

10   Buy me a bar of milk c_ _ _ _ _ _ _ _, please.

11   My Dad has a valuable stamp c_ _ _ _ _ _ _ _ _.

12   Sir Christopher Wren d_ _ _ _ _ _ _ St Paul's Cathedral.

13   The prize in the c_ _ _ _ _ _ _ _ _ _ is a silver cup.

14   Tom was badly injured in the road a_ _ _ _ _ _ _.

15   Computers will not f_ _ _ _ _ _ _ unless programmed.

16   The runner finished the race in a state of c_ _ _ _ _ _ _.

17   Make a New Year r_ _ _ _ _ _ _ _ _ and keep it.

18   The survivors were put into temporary a_ _ _ _ _ _ _ _ _ _ _ _ _.

19   Mr Hertz has not lost his German a_ _ _ _ _ _.

20   A car needs an a_ _ _ _ _ for CB radio.

collision occasion excursion division expansion revision	

Complete these sentences. Use the words in the box.

1 John found the d _ _ _ _ _ _ sums rather difficult.
2 As it was a special o _ _ _ _ _ _ _ we had a party.
3 Both cars were damaged in the c _ _ _ _ _ _ _ _ .
4 Paul must do more r _ _ _ _ _ _ to pass the test.
5 When pipes freeze the e _ _ _ _ _ _ _ of the water bursts the pipe.
6 The club planned an e _ _ _ _ _ _ _ _ to London.

---

television confusion conclusion vision
decision possession extension discussion

Place the words in italics in their correct sentences.

1 You need an *conclusion* ladder to reach the roof.
2 The street was in mad *television* with people screaming.
3 The referee's *vision* is final.
4 The play had a spectacular *extension*.
5 The speakers had a very long *possession*.
6 The blow on Ted's head gave him double *decision*.
7 I am in *discussion* of certain information.
8 Samantha watches *confusion* for hours at a time.

procession   permission   succession
transmission   mission   obsession
impression   admission

Complete these sentences. Use the words in the box.

1   The cavalry's m _ _ _ _ _ _ was to attack the
    Indians.
2   Press the shape into the clay to make an
    i _ _ _ _ _ _ _ _ _.
3   The long p _ _ _ _ _ _ _ _ _ wound along the street.
4   Tidiness is an o _ _ _ _ _ _ _ _ of Mrs Lark's.
5   The journey was a s _ _ _ _ _ _ _ _ _ of mishaps.
6   The charge for a _ _ _ _ _ _ _ _ will be 50p.
7   You need Mr Grimm's p _ _ _ _ _ _ _ _ _ to leave.
8   We begin t _ _ _ _ _ _ _ _ _ _ _ of the new T.V.
    programmes soon.

commission   fission   remission
permission   admission

*Remove the letter **t** from each word*
*and add **ssion** to make a new word.*

1   remit
2   commit
3   admit
4   fit
5   permit

Look up the meaning of each word. Write three
sentences using three of the words on this page.

> **valour   value   vacuum
> vagrant   vacant   valuable**

Complete these sentences. Use the words in the box.

1   Lock all v _ _ _ _ _ _ _ items in the safe.
2   The old house has been v _ _ _ _ _ for a year.
3   The stolen goods were of no v _ _ _ _.
4   We need a new bag on the v _ _ _ _ _ cleaner.
5   A tramp is sometimes called a v _ _ _ _ _ _.
6   Medals are awarded for v _ _ _ _ _.

> **artistically   gradually   gracefully
> eventually   especially   faithfully
> truthfully**

*Complete these sentences.
Use the words in the box.*

1   The letter ended with: 'Yours f _ _ _ _ _ _ _ _ _'.
2   Search carefully and you'll find it e _ _ _ _ _ _ _ _ _.
3   The water g _ _ _ _ _ _ _ _ wore away the stone.
4   The lawyer said, "Answer t _ _ _ _ _ _ _ _ _".
5   She walked as g _ _ _ _ _ _ _ _ _ as any model.
6   The book cover was a _ _ _ _ _ _ _ _ _ _ _ designed.
7   Jenny was e _ _ _ _ _ _ _ _ _ careful when carrying
    the tray.

| emptiness holiness sadness loneliness happiness business wickedness cheerfulness mildness |  |

These words are adjectives. Change them into **nouns** *by adding* **ness**. *Remember — words that end in* **y** *change the* **y** *to* **i** *before adding* **ness**.

1	wicked	4	holy	7	empty
2	lonely	5	cheerful	8	happy
3	busy	6	sad	9	mild

Complete these sentences using the words you have made.

1 The baby brought great h_____ to the family.

2 Many acts of w_____ took place during the war.

3 Francis was made a saint because of his h_____.

4 Tim's face showed his s_____ and he wept.

5 Jesse Boot built up a great b_____ empire.

6 The desert stretched in front, nothing but e_____.

7 He showed c_____ all through his illness.

8 Feel the m_____ in these soft suds.

9 Robinson Crusoe suffered great l_____ on his island.

Mini Revision pages 13 to 16

confusion cheerfulness valuable
procession vacuum admission especially
designed permission excursion
gradually television decision happiness
vacant faithfully division obsession

Complete these sentences. Use the words in the box.

1 Do the addition sums then the d _ _ _ _ _ _ _ sums.

2 You have smashed a v _ _ _ _ _ _ _ antique.

3 Simon was sad but tried to show
   c _ _ _ _ _ _ _ _ _ _ _.

4 The school went on a day e _ _ _ _ _ _ _ _.

5 You can learn a lot by watching t _ _ _ _ _ _ _ _ _.

6 You need p _ _ _ _ _ _ _ _ _ to park there.

7 Everyone rushed about causing c _ _ _ _ _ _ _ _.

8 The architect d _ _ _ _ _ _ _ a new house.

9 The price of a _ _ _ _ _ _ _ _ to the zoo is high.

10 The old butler had served his Lordship
    f _ _ _ _ _ _ _ _ _.

11 Smile and show everyone your h _ _ _ _ _ _ _ _.

12 Mum had to buy a new v _ _ _ _ _ cleaner.

13 The p _ _ _ _ _ _ _ _ _ marched along and the band
    played.

14 The house is v _ _ _ _ _ and we can move in now.

15 Everyone must work e _ _ _ _ _ _ _ _ _ hard to
    finish the job.

16 Mr Brown will give his d _ _ _ _ _ _ _ tomorrow.

17 Mary's face g _ _ _ _ _ _ _ _ went white, then she
    fainted.

18 Fishing is an o _ _ _ _ _ _ _ _ of Mark's, not a
    hobby.

soft
g

*The words in italics are in the wrong sentences.
Rewrite the sentences correctly. Use the words
in the box.*

1   The *margin* told his men to stand still.
2   William had a sudden *average* to scratch his leg.
3   The *religion* on each page should be 4cm wide.
4   Christianity is the main *village* of Europe.
5   Shaw was of *urge* height with dark hair.
6   My aunt lives in a *sergeant* in Hampshire.

purchase   turban   murder   turquoise
surface   pursue   turkey   figure

ur

Complete these words by adding **ur**.
The clues will help you.

1   To kill someone deliberately   m _ _ der
2   The top of something   s _ _ face
3   A light greenish blue colour   t _ _ quoise
4   To buy   p _ _ chase
5   To chase   p _ _ sue
6   A bird eaten at Christmas   t _ _ key
7   A number or shape   fig _ _ e
8   A piece of cloth wound round the head   t _ _ ban

agreement amazement arrangement	
judgement contentment government	

Complete these sentences. Use the words in the box.

1 The driver made a bad error of j_____.

2 I am in complete _g_____ with the decision.

3 The well fed cat was in a state of c_____.

4 The crowd watched the feat in stunned
   _m_____.

5 I made an a_____ to meet you.

6 The Prime Minister leads the g_____.

Decode the words below using this key.

a = <   o = ⌐   t = ₹

d = ⊏   p = Ⴇ   v = ʌ

e = ⍵   r = ⌀   ment = ∾

n = ×

1   Ⴇ < ʌ ⍵ ∾

2   ⊏ ⍵ Ⴇ < ⌀ ₹ ∾

3   < Ⴇ < ⌀ ₹ ∾

4   ₹ ⌀ ⍵ < ₹ ∾

5   ⌐ ⌀ × < ∾

6   ₹ ⌐ ⌀ ∾

professor	terrific	referee
merrier	dessert	possessed
preferred	profession	

assorted

Complete these sentences. Use the words in the box.

1 Medicine is a great p_____n.
2 The r_____ awarded a penalty to Leeds.
3 Mr Hunt is a p_____r of modern languages.
4 My Dad said he __e_____ coffee to tea.
5 We had chocolate mousse for d_____.
6 He swore that he had never _o_____ a gun.
7 The party grew m_____ as the evening went on.
8 The bomb went off with a t_____ explosion.

| hymn | column | solemn |
| condemn | autumn | |

mn

Complete these words. They all end in **mn**. *Match the words you make to their correct meaning.*

1 conde__   1 a pillar
2 colu__   2 a religious song
3 autu__   3 a season
4 hy__   4 serious
5 sole__   5 to blame

Complete these words by adding **app** or **opp**.
Match the words you make to the clues.

app
and
opp

1	___roach	1	To be grateful
2	___onent	2	Black is ? to white
3	___roval	3	Equipment
4	___ose	4	Enemy
5	___reciate	5	The desire for food
6	___arently	6	To move closer
7	___osite	7	To stand up against
8	___etite	8	A part of the gut
9	___endix	9	Clapping
10	___ortunity	10	To come into view
11	___rentice	11	To show agreement
12	___ress	12	A beginner
13	___lause	13	To bully
14	___ear	14	A chance
15	___aratus	15	Seemingly

Decode the words below using this key.

a = N	i = Ƃ	s = ☌	pp = ϴ
l = Ɵ	o = ᴕ	t = ⌁	
e = ʌ	n = ⊠	y = ☌	

1 N ϴ Ɵ ʌ   **4** ᴕ ϴ ᴕ ☌ Ƃ ⌁ ʌ

2 N ϴ Ɵ ☌   **5** ᴕ ϴ ᴕ ☌ ʌ

3 N ϴ ʌ N Ɵ   **6** ᴕ ϴ ᴕ ⊠ ʌ ⊠ ⌁

Test Yourself 2

Complete these sentences. Each dash stands for a letter.

1   The r _ _ _ _ _ _ blew his whistle for half time.
2   Some Indian men wear a t _ _ _ _ _.
3   The s _ _ _ _ _ _ _ had three stripes on his arm.
4   I knew we would l _ _ _ with Wilfred in goal.
5   Ballet dancers always move g _ _ _ _ _ _ _ _ _.
6   I cleaned the carpet with the v _ _ _ _ _ cleaner.
7   Dan is always hungry; he has a huge
    a _ _ _ _ _ _ _.
8   Everyone did r _ _ _ _ _ _ _ for the examination.
9   The judge s _ _ _ _ _ _ _ _ the man to life in prison.
10 We all said a prayer and sang a h _ _ _.
11 Jesus Christ founded the Christian r _ _ _ _ _ _ _.
12 Dad gave Bill p _ _ _ _ _ _ _ _ _ to stay out late.
13 Only ticket holders will be allowed a _ _ _ _ _ _ _ _.
14 Both cars were damaged in the c _ _ _ _ _ _ _ _.
15 There was not much a _ _ _ _ _ _ _ at the end of
    the concert.
16 Another word for 'buy' is p _ _ _ _ _ _ _.
17 The a _ _ _ _ _ _ of three, five and seven, is five.
18 Happiness is the opposite of s _ _ _ _ _ _.
19 The spy was sent on a secret m _ _ _ _ _ _.
20 Wide is the o _ _ _ _ _ _ _ of narrow.

insurance	laziest	ambulance
handiest	ignorance	luckiest
heaviest	jolliest	dirtiest
remembrance	tidiest	busiest
funniest	assistance	nuisance

iest
and
ance

Complete these words by adding **iest** *or* **ance**.

Examples: prett + iest = prettiest

appear + ance = appearance

1	assist	6	dirt	11	funn
2	laz	7	tid	12	ignor
3	hand	8	nuis	13	joll
4	ambul	9	heav	14	luck
5	insur	10	bus	15	remembr

Complete these sentences using one of the words you have made.

1   The a_ _ _ _ _ _ _ _ drove off with its siren blaring.

2   Father took out a big life i_ _ _ _ _ _ _ _ policy.

3   Emma is the t_ _ _ _ _ _ girl I know.

4   We buy poppies in r_ _ _ _ _ _ _ _ _ _ of dead soldiers.

5   Wilfred is by far the l_ _ _ _ _ _ boy in the school.

6   The comedian was the f_ _ _ _ _ _ _ I have ever seen.

| thief patient tiers relieve |
| priest sieve fierce handkerchief |

(ie)

Complete these sentences. Use the words in the box.

1 The battle was a f_ _ _ _ _ one.
2 The cinema seats were arranged in t_ _ _ _.
3 The p_ _ _ _ _ conducted a Mass.
4 The t_ _ _ _ hid the jewels in his coat.
5 John wiped his eyes with his h_ _ _ _ _ _ _ _ _ _.
6 The nurse told the p_ _ _ _ _ _ to stay in bed.
7 We had to s_ _ _ _ the flour to remove lumps.
8 She had an injection to r_ _ _ _ _ _ the pain.

| audience experience patience |
| conscience convenience |

Complete these sentences. Use the words in the box.

1 The difficult jigsaw required great p_ _ _ _ _ _ _ _.
2 We eat a great deal of c_ _ _ _ _ _ _ _ _ _ foods.
3 Visiting New York will be a wonderful
   e_ _ _ _ _ _ _ _ _.
4 The a_ _ _ _ _ _ _ applauded the singer.
5 Our c_ _ _ _ _ _ _ _ _ tells us when an action
   is wrong.

y

sounds like

ee

| apology | commentary | activity |
| authority | community | busily |

The words in italic print are in the wrong sentences. Rewrite the sentences correctly.

1   There was a lot of *commentary* in the office.
2   A policeman has the *community* to stop traffic.
3   The class were all *apology* working.
4   The new Health Centre will serve the whole *authority*.
5   We could not hear the tennis *busily*.
6   Alan sent a letter of *activity* for being so rude.

| legible | horrible | impossible |
| terrible | responsible | invisible |

(ible)

Crack the code and write out the words correctly.
All the words end in the same four letters.
To help you: a = 1   b = 2   c = 3   up to z = 26.

1   20 : 5 : 18 : 18 : 9 : 2 : 12 : 5
2   8 : 15 : 18 : 18 : 9 : 2 : 12 : 5
3   9 : 14 : 22 : 9 : 19 : 9 : 2 : 12 : 5
4   12 : 5 : 7 : 9 : 2 : 12 : 5
5   9 : 13 : 16 : 15 : 19 : 19 : 9 : 2 : 12 : 15
6   18 : 5 : 19 : 16 : 15 : 14 : 19 : 9 : 2 : 12 : 15

persuade	different	sermon	prettier
perform	perfume	preserve	deserve

Fill in the grid with the answers to the clues.
Use the words in the box.

1 Keep from going rotten
2 To act
3 Sweet smelling
4 More than pretty

5 Get someone to agree
6 Not the same as
7 Be entitled to
8 A talk by a priest

1	p	–	–	–	–	–	–	–
2	p	–	–	–	–	–	–	
3	p	–	–	–	–	–	–	
4	p	–	–	–	–	–	–	
5	p	–	–	–	–	–	–	
6	d	–	–	–	–	–	–	–
7	d	–	–	–	–	–		
8	s	–	–	–	–	–		

omit	obliged	overturn	overtake
opinion	overture	oasis	odour

Complete these sentences. Use the words in the box.

1 An _a___ is a fertile place in the desert.
2 The orchestra started playing the _____e.
3 The politician gave an _p_____ on the crisis.
4 The chemical gave off a strong _d___.
5 It is dangerous to _____k_ on a bend.
6 The rioters tried to _____n the car.
7 We had to _m__ the third sentence.
8 We are _b_____ to drive on the left.

Mini Revision

pages 23 to 26

> **commentary** **ignorance** **ambulance**
> **sermon** **ample** **invisible** **apology**
> **patient** **conscience** **nuisance**
> **fierce** **legible** **handkerchief** **patience**
> **overturn** **busiest** **insurance** **thief**

Complete these sentences. Use the words in the box.

1 The a _ _ _ _ _ _ _ _ driver gave the boy first aid.

2 Market day is the b _ _ _ _ _ _ day of the week.

3 The sign said 'Beware of the f _ _ _ _ _ dog'.

4 The p _ _ _ _ _ _ is very ill, I'm afraid.

5 The stone was too heavy for Jim to o _ _ _ _ _ _ _.

6 Amanda, do stop being such a n _ _ _ _ _ _ _.

7 The blushing woman wished she was
   i _ _ _ _ _ _ _ _.

8 He will have that crime on his c _ _ _ _ _ _ _ _ _.

9 The judge sentenced the t _ _ _ _ to prison.

10 The model took time and p _ _ _ _ _ _ _ to make.

11 The vicar gave a long s _ _ _ _ _ at church.

12 Take out holiday i _ _ _ _ _ _ _ _ when going
   abroad.

13 The match c _ _ _ _ _ _ _ _ _ starts at midday.

14 There was a _ _ _ _ food for the party.

15 Show your manners and not your i _ _ _ _ _ _ _ _.

16 I have been silly and must offer an a _ _ _ _ _ _.

17 Craig's handwriting is hardly l _ _ _ _ _ _.

18 Emily wiped her nose with the new
   h _ _ _ _ _ _ _ _ _ _.

epilogue monologue catalogue
synagogue dialogue intrigue
fatigue rogue vague league

Complete the words by adding **gue.** *The clues will help you.*
Match the words to the clues.

1 A Jewish church   va _ _ _
2 One person speaking   ro _ _ _
3 Great weariness   lea _ _ _
4 A dishonest person   fati _ _ _
5 Sometimes written after
   the end of a story   epilo _ _ _
6 Not definite   dialo _ _ _
7 People talking to one another   intri _ _ _
8 A book listing things   monolo _ _ _
9 Football teams compete in a   catalo _ _ _
10 Plotting and scheming   synago _ _ _

deceived receipt deceit
conceited ceiling

Complete these sentences. Use the words in the box.

1 Tom is an unpleasant and c _ _ _ _ _ _ _ _ person.
2 Ask for a r _ _ _ _ _ _ for what you pay.
3 You misled and d _ _ _ _ _ _ _ me completely.
4 How could you be capable of such d _ _ _ _ _ ,
   you cheat.
5 Tony painted the c _ _ _ _ _ _ of his bedroom.

| foreigner seize weird reign leisure | |

Complete these sentences. Use the words in the box.

1 Queen Victoria's r _ _ _ _ lasted for sixty years.
2 We saw the dog s _ _ _ _ the rabbit by the neck.
3 The lights cast w _ _ _ _ shapes on to the walls.
4 We should spend our l _ _ _ _ _ _ time usefully.
5 The f _ _ _ _ _ _ _ _ could not speak any English.

| deficient sufficient ancient client efficient | |

Complete these sentences. Use the words in the box.

1 The Pyramids are really a _ _ _ _ _ _ tombs.
2 The lawyer was ready to see his next c _ _ _ _ _ .
3 Tim did not get s _ _ _ _ _ _ _ _ marks to pass the test.
4 A robot may be more e _ _ _ _ _ _ _ _ than a man.
5 If our diet is d _ _ _ _ _ _ _ _ in vitamins it can affect our health.

| theatre centre litre metre | |

Complete these sentences. Use the words in the box.

1 Ask Pierre for a l _ _ _ _ of wine.
2 Shakespeare is on at the t _ _ _ _ _ _ this week.
3 Sam can jump a m _ _ _ _ further than Mark.
4 The city c _ _ _ _ _ is closed to traffic.

| system   hysterical   mystery   crystal |

y

sounds like
short i

Complete these words by adding **y.**

1   s_stem
2   m_stery
3   h_sterical
4   cr_stal

| choir   chorus   orchestra
character   scheme |

ch

sounds like
k or c

Complete these words by adding **ch.**

1   __aracter
2   __oir
3   __orus
4   s__eme
5   or__estra

*Use eight of the words you have made to complete
these sentences.*

1   The o_____ played Viennese waltzes.
2   The assistant dropped the c_____ vase.
3   Mum was h_____ when she heard of
   the accident.
4   Only Sherlock Holmes could solve the m_____.
5   We have a new s_____ for ordering the books.
6   The old man was a shifty looking c_____.
7   We now have a s_____ to help disabled people.
8   Eric has a fine voice and sings in the c____.

descend   scented   ascent
ascend   descent

Use the words in the box to answer the clues.
Copy out the puzzle and fill it in.

Across

1 To go up
2 The journey downwards

Down

1 The journey upwards
2 To go down
3 Smelling sweetly

fascinated   science   scenery
muscle   scissors

Complete these sentences. Use the words in the box.

1 The baby is too young to use s_ _ _ _ _ _ _.
2 The footballer pulled a m_ _ _ _ _ during training.
3 The _ _e_ _ _ _ in the Lake District is magnificent.
4 I enjoy learning s_ _ _ _ _ _.
5 The children were f_ _ _ _ _ _ _ _ _ by the magician.

Test Yourself 3

pages 23 to 31

Complete these sentences. Each dash stands for a letter.

1 Lucy bought a l _ _ _ _ of milk.
2 The terrified woman became h _ _ _ _ _ _ _ _.
3 The a _ _ _ _ _ _ _ _ rushed to pick up the injured people.
4 The nurse made the p _ _ _ _ _ _ more comfortable.
5 George found it i _ _ _ _ _ _ _ _ _ to tell a lie.
6 Donald watched the fly walking on the c _ _ _ _ _ _.
7 The dancers wore strange costumes and w _ _ _ _ masks.
8 There was wild applause from the a _ _ _ _ _ _ _.
9 All the Jews wore their hats in the s _ _ _ _ _ _ _ _.
10 Our industry must be more e _ _ _ _ _ _ _ _ to survive.
11 Laura had the crime on her c _ _ _ _ _ _ _ _ _.
12 The climbers began the d _ _ _ _ _ _ from the mountain.
13 You owe Peter an a _ _ _ _ _ _ for being so rude.
14 The birds kept me awake with their dawn c _ _ _ _ _.
15 Clean this room, it's the d _ _ _ _ _ _ _ place I've seen.
16 Wilfred was f _ _ _ _ _ _ _ _ _ by the monkeys.
17 A very strange o _ _ _ _ arose from the vegetables.
18 Perhaps Cliff can p _ _ _ _ _ _ _ Harry to come too.
19 Cut the material with a pair of s _ _ _ _ _ _ _ _.
20 If you need a _ _ _ _ _ _ _ _ _ with the job, call me.

32

general	garage	gentleness	hinges
college	logical	original	gorgeous
sponge	image	genius	imagine
sausage	emergency	generous	

soft

g

Complete these words by adding the soft letter **g.**
Use the word box to help you.

1 colle_e	6 _eneral	11 emer_ency
2 hin_es	7 lo_ical	12 ori_inal
3 sausa_e	8 _enius	13 ima_ine
4 spon_e	9 _enerous	14 gara_e
5 _entleness	10 gor_eous	15 ima_e

garage	sponge	generous
general	hinges	emergency

Use the six words in the box to complete these sentences.

1 All the e _ _ _ _ _ _ _ services attended the
  accident.
2 Dad took his car to the g _ _ _ _ _ for repair.
3 The door h _ _ _ _ _ were broken.
4 Mum iced the _p _ _ _ _ cake.
5 The man was thanked for his _e _ _ _ _ _ _
  donation.
6 The _ _ _ _ _ _l took the salute as the army
  marched past.

Write down the odd word out in each group.
Say why it is the odd one out.

assorted

1 surprise, comfortable, surface, surgeon
2 worrying, carrying, miserable, copying
3 soil, capable, noise, join, foil
4 syllable, tailor, afraid, raise, faint
5 cheap, steal, reliable, beach
6 whisper, whip, valuable, which
7 office, difficult, reasonable, officers
8 probable, window, hollow, shallow

| answer sword wreck wrist |
| wreckage wrench wrestling |

silent
W

Complete these sentences. Use the words in the box.

1 The diver found the w＿＿＿＿ of the galleon.
2 The telephone is ringing, please a＿＿＿＿＿ it.
3 The w＿＿＿＿＿＿＿ of the collision was removed by police.
4 Emily gave the handle a sudden w＿＿＿＿＿ and broke it.
5 King Arthur had a s＿＿＿＿ named Excalibur.
6 We watched the w＿＿＿＿＿＿＿＿ on T.V.
7 Jenny sprained her w＿＿＿＿ when she fell.

34

excellent excerpt excuse
excel except excited

Complete these sentences. Use the words in the box.

1   All the children _ _ _ _p_ Wayne took part.
2   The choir sang an _ _ _ _r_ _ from the 'Mikado'.
3   Elizabeth had an _ _ _e_ _ _ _ _ school report.
4   Tom has always been able to e_ _ _ _ at swimming.
5   Christmas makes the children e_ _ _ _ _d.
6   Have you a good e_ _ _ _e for being late?

cycle medicine bicycle proceed
tricycle innocent plumber

Complete these sentences. Use the words in the box.

1   Little Kim had a new t_ _ _ _ _ _ _ for Christmas.
2   My b_ _ _ _ _ _ has a flat tyre.
3   Sometimes Dad allows me to c_ _ _ _ to school.
4   Take this m_ _ _ _ _ _ _ twice a day.
5   The p_ _ _ _ _ _ mended the leaking pipe.
6   Mike is completely i_ _ _ _ _ _ _ of the charge.
7   Go to the mill and p_ _ _ _ _ _ in a southerly
    direction.

colour	humour	favourite
labour	honour	

The words in italics are in the wrong sentences.
Rewrite the sentences correctly.

1 I like the *labour* of Lucy's new dress.
2 Alison has a very good sense of *honour*.
3 Erroll's *colour* meal is fish and chips.
4 On my word of *humour* I am not lying.
5 The prisoner received two years' hard *favourite*.

Complete these parts of words by adding **al.**
The clues will help you.

1 A celebration   festiv _ _
2 Not ordinary   unusu _ _
3 A big church   cathedr _ _
4 Opposite of departure   arriv _ _
5 To do with the body   physic _ _
6 The head of a college   princip _ _
7 To do with politics   politic _ _
8 Straight line from left to right   horizont _ _
9 Comes out at night   nocturn _ _
10 More than one   sever _ _
11 Service for a dead person   funer _ _
12 Useful   practic _ _

Mini Revision

pages 33 to 36

nocturnal excellent wreckage syllables practical colour sword plumber college humour funeral genius except bicycle arrival answer capable medicine

Complete these sentences. Use the words in the box.

1 My sister is going to c_____ next year.

2 Yellow is the fashionable c_____ this year.

3 Everyone was allowed to go e_____ poor John.

4 I expect an a_____ to my question.

5 Baby is making e_____ progress now.

6 Take this m_____ every day.

7 Mr Grimm has no sense of h_____.

8 Hedgehogs are n_____ animals.

9 The knight pointed his s____ at the dragon.

10 Dad is fond of p_____ jokes.

11 Firemen cut the victim from the w_____.

12 John had a new b_____ for his birthday.

13 The word 'picture' has two s_____ in it.

14 Claire is quite c_____ of cooking the meal.

15 Many famous people attended his f_____.

16 The aircraft's time of a_____ has been changed.

17 Jeremy is a postive g_____ at maths.

18 Call the p_____ as the pipe has burst.

Complete these words by adding **ous** *or* **ious.**

ous
and
ious

1 numer____
2 vic_____
3 var_____
4 marvell____
5 ridicul____
6 suspic_____
7 tremend____
8 prec_____

9   humor____
10 delic_____
11 enorm____
12 poison____
13 ser_____
14 caut_____
15 jeal____
16 gener____

Use five of the words to complete these sentences.

1 Jill has a s_____ illness, I'm afraid.
2 The crown was a mass of p_____ jewels.
3 The cake had a most _e_____ taste.
4 Cyanide is a very _o_____ substance.
5 The judge said the attack was _i_____.

| humorous cautious numerous |
| marvellous enormous ridiculous |

Use the words in the box to answer the clues.

1 Another word for many
2 Very silly
3 Funny
4 Taking great care
5 Wonderful, full of marvel
6 Huge, massive

society   electricity   council
decide   pencil   necessity

Complete these sentences. Use the words in the box.

1   Most home appliances are powered by
    e _ _ _ _ _ _ _ _ _ _.
2   Join a choral s _ _ _ _ _ _ if you want to sing.
3   Mrs Lumley wants to be elected to the c _ _ _ _ _ _.
4   Mistakes in p _ _ _ _ _ can easily be rubbed out.
5   Please d _ _ _ _ _ now whether you are going or not.
6   A washing machine is a n _ _ _ _ _ _ _ _.

stationary   secretary   temporary
anniversary   adversary

Complete these sentences. Use the words in the box.

1   We celebrate our wedding a _ _ _ _ _ _ _ _ _ _
    today.
2   Jane is applying for a job as a s _ _ _ _ _ _ _ _.
3   The s _ _ _ _ _ _ _ _ _ car was blocking the road.
4   The school is being used as a t _ _ _ _ _ _ _ _ shelter.
5   David's great a _ _ _ _ _ _ _ _ was Goliath.

chalet   thorough   xylophone
picturesque   exaggerated

Complete these sentences. Use the words in the box.

1   Sam waved his arms in an e _ _ _ _ _ _ _ _ _ _ way.
2   Dominic played a tune on the x _ _ _ _ _ _ _ _.
3   Give your hair a t _ _ _ _ _ _ _ brushing.
4   We went back to our c _ _ _ _ _ to change.
5   The view was very p _ _ _ _ _ _ _ _ _ _.

expanse   exercise   explain   expense
extreme   extend   exhaust
exclaim   extravagant   excuse

*Crack this code and add **ex** to the beginning of each*
group of letters to make complete words.
To help you: a = _b_   c = _/3_   n = _∅_   p = **1**   r = _G_   s = _ZZ_

1	**1**	e	∅	ZZ	e			6	**1**	_b_	∅	ZZ	e
2	t	_G_	e	m	e			7	**1**	l	_b_	i	∅
3	h	_b_	u	ZZ	t			8	/3	u	ZZ	e	
4	t	_G_	_b_	v	_b_	g	_b_∅ t	9	t	e	∅	d	
5	e	**1**	/3	i	ZZ	e		10	/3	l	_b_	i	m

---

mileage   noticeable
likeable   manageable

Complete these sentences. Use the words in the box.

1   Tom was a polite and l_ _ _ _ _ _ _ boy.
2   The car had covered a high m_ _ _ _ _ _.
3   The scar on Lyn's face was not n_ _ _ _ _ _ _ _ _.
4   That dog is not m_ _ _ _ _ _ _ _ and must go.

---

treasure   measure   pleasure   leisure

Complete these sentences. Use the words in the box.

1   It is a great p_ _ _ _ _ _ _ to meet you at last.
2   Clint loves to sail in his l_ _ _ _ _ _ time.
3   Blackbeard buried the t_ _ _ _ _ _ _ on the beach.
4   Will you m_ _ _ _ _ _ my waist for me, please?

| unusual union unity useful |
| universal influenza united universe |

The words in italics are in the wrong sentences.
Rewrite the sentences correctly.

1   Everybody is *influenza* in opposing the new road.
2   The men formed a trade *universal*.
3   The doctor thought Tom had *united*.
4   The candle cast strange and *union* shadows.
5   The alien came from the other side of the *unity*.
6   A hammer is a *unusual* tool.
7   The effects of the disease were almost *useful*.
8   If we stick together then *universe* is strength.

| squirrel squeak square squall |
| squid squabble squirm squeeze |
| squash squirt squat squeal |

Crack this code and write out the words correctly.
All the words begin with the same three letters.
To help you: s = 1   q = 7   u = 4   a = 2

1   1.7.4.2.s.h.
2   1.7.4.2.b.b.l.e.
3   1.7.4.e.2.l.
4   1.7.4.e.2.k.
5   1.7.4.2.r.e.
6   1.7.4.i.r.r.e.l.

7   1.7.4.e.e.z.e.
8   1.7.4.2.t.
9   1.7.4.i.r.m.
10   1.7.4.i.r.t.
11   1.7.4.i.d.
12   1.7.4.2.l.l.

Test Yourself 4

pages 33 to 41

Complete these sentences. Each dash stands for a letter.

1 Give this letter to Sam and wait for an a _ _ _ _ _.

2 Sharpen your p _ _ _ _ _, it is blunt.

3 Closing the road is only t _ _ _ _ _ _ _ _, not permanent.

4 The actor performed an e _ _ _ _ _ _ from 'Macbeth'.

5 Ben's f _ _ _ _ _ _ _ _ magazine is the 'New Musical Express'.

6 The car's e _ _ _ _ _ _ pipe needs renewing.

7 I would like beans, s _ _ _ _ _ _ _, and chips, please.

8 Wilfred is a rogue but he is quite l _ _ _ _ _ _ _.

9 We will go to the f _ _ _ _ _ _ _ of folk music.

10 Everyone in the factory belongs to a trade u _ _ _ _.

11 Gran thinks the m _ _ _ _ _ _ _ will make her better.

12 This armchair is very c _ _ _ _ _ _ _ _ _ _.

13 My uncle keeps his car in a concrete g _ _ _ _ _.

14 I want a s _ _ _ _ _ table, not a round one.

15 Fred is a g _ _ _ _ _ with computers.

16 Don't be r _ _ _ _ _ _ _ _ _, I haven't got £1000!

17 Take care, that toadstool is p _ _ _ _ _ _ _ _.

18 Stop moaning Gary, you are so m _ _ _ _ _ _ _ _.

19 One day, space ships will explore the u _ _ _ _ _ _ _.

20 I find this b _ _ _ _ _ _ very hard to pedal.

frequent	century	theatre
recent	similar	tourist
enthusiasm	machinery	

Complete these sentences. Use the words in the box.

1   We are living in the twentieth c _ _ _ _ _ _.

2   The factory is full of noisy m _ _ _ _ _ _ _ _.

3   The American t _ _ _ _ _ _ asked the way.

4   Linda makes f _ _ _ _ _ _ _ visits to her aunt.

5   The twins are s _ _ _ _ _ _ but not identical.

6   Alan practised his music with e _ _ _ _ _ _ _ _ _.

7   The accident was r _ _ _ _ _ and he is still poorly.

8   Our t _ _ _ _ _ _ presents a new play every week.

request	mosquito	conquer
quantity	quality	quarter	liquid
quill	quarrel	question

Complete these words. The clues will help you.
Use the words in the box.

1   A fourth part   _ _ _ r _ _ _

2   A fierce argument   _ _ _ _ _ _ l

3   Water is a ?   _ _ _ _ _ d

4   Ask for   r _ _ _ _ _ _

5   How good something is   _ _ a _ _ _ _

6   One expects an answer to a ?   _ _ _ s _ _ _ _

7   Take by force   c _ _ _ _ _ _

8   Old type of pen   _ _ i _ _

9   Small flying insect that bites   m _ _ _ _ _ _ _

10   Amount of something   _ _ a _ _ _ _ _

Complete these sentences. Use the words in the box.

1 Columbus crossed the o____ to America.
2 Pull six sticks of r_____ to make a pie.
3 The wreck is marked by a b___.
4 The y____ has a fibre-glass hull.
5 The old man is very ill with p_____.
6 A story in dance and music is a b_____.
7 The rusty old ship is unloading at the q___.
8 Rita has a wonderful sense of r_____.

**surgeon pigeon dungeon
luncheon truncheon**

eo

Crack this code and work out the words correctly.
To help you:

c = ∧   d = >   g = <   h = ∇   i = ◊
l = ᴎ   p = ⊩   n = ⬤   r = ꝗ   s = ⊕
t = ᴎ   u = ⋆   eon = ⟲

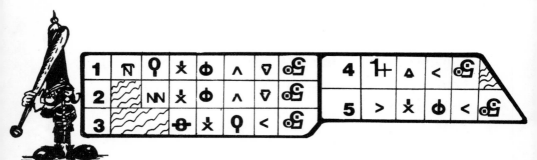

Mini Revision

pages 43 and 44

century   frequent   ocean   truncheon
pigeon   similar   dungeon   tourist   question
machinery   buoy   conquer   surgeon   yacht
rhubarb   liquid   ballet   quality

Complete these sentences. Use the words in the box.

1   Hitler set out to c_ _ _ _ _ _ the world.

2   This r_ _ _ _ _ _ is very sour.

3   Space rockets are powered by l_ _ _ _ _ oxygen.

4   My dress is s_ _ _ _ _ _ in colour to yours.

5   The constable drew his t_ _ _ _ _ _ _ _.

6   The boy could not answer the q_ _ _ _ _ _ _.

7   Vanessa wants to be a b_ _ _ _ _ dancer.

8   The poor man was chained in a dark d_ _ _ _ _ _.

9   Our troops sent a message by carrier p_ _ _ _ _.

10   The Tower of London is a t_ _ _ _ _ _ attraction.

11   The b_ _ _ marking the reef has a bell on it.

12   The builders brought in heavy m_ _ _ _ _ _ _ _.

13   The little boat was tossed about on the o_ _ _ _.

14   The s_ _ _ _ _ _ decided to operate.

15   The coach makes f_ _ _ _ _ _ _ stops on its journey.

16   One hundred years is called a c_ _ _ _ _ _.

17   The y_ _ _ _ had red sails.

18   The material in his coat is very poor q_ _ _ _ _ _.

benefit   twelfth   pyjamas
volunteer   cheque   separate
awkward   necessary
benefactor   peculiar

Crack this code and write out the words correctly.
To help you: a = 26   b = 25   c = 24   and z = 1.

1   7.4.22.15.21.7.19.
2   11.2.17.26.14.26.8.
3   11.22.24.6.15.18.26.9.
4   25.22.13.22.21.18.7.
5   25.22.13.22.21.26.24.7.12.9.
6   26.4.16.4.26.9.23.
7   13.22.24.22.8.8.26.9.2.
8   8.22.11.26.9.26.7.22.
9   5.12.15.6.13.7.22.22.9.
10   24.19.22.10.6.22.

volunteer   pyjamas   unique   bouquet
twelfth   separate   antique

Use the words in the box to complete these sentences.

1   John came t _ _ _ _ _ _ in the marathon.
2   Each guest has a s _ _ _ _ _ _ _ bedroom.
3   The vase Wilfred broke was a valuable a _ _ _ _ _ _.
4   Harry put on his new p _ _ _ _ _ _ ready for bed.
5   Each Japanese pilot was a v _ _ _ _ _ _ _ _.
6   Joan's collection of books is quite u _ _ _ _ _.
7   The dancer was given a b _ _ _ _ _ _ of flowers.

pheasant xylophone telephone orphan triumph photograph amphibian atmosphere	

Complete these words. Use the words in the box.

1 A picture taken with a camera   ph _ _ _ _ _ _ _ _

2 Air surrounding the earth   at _ _ _ _ _ _ _ _

3 Can live on land or in water   am _ _ _ _ _ _ _

4 A victory   tr _ _ _ _ _

5 We talk to others on this   te _ _ _ _ _ _ _

6 Musical instrument   xy _ _ _ _ _ _ _

7 A bird   ph _ _ _ _ _ _

8 A child who has no parents   or _ _ _ _

neighbour parallel souvenir neighbourhood mysterious	

Complete these sentences. Use the words in the box.

1 Our next door n _ _ _ _ _ _ _ _ has a beautiful garden.

2 The old cave was dark and m _ _ _ _ _ _ _ _ _ _.

3 Auntie wanted to buy a s _ _ _ _ _ _ _ of her visit.

4 Railway lines are always p _ _ _ _ _ _ _ _.

5 The whole n _ _ _ _ _ _ _ _ _ _ _ _ was woken up by the din.

Just for YOU

Complete these sentences. Each dash stands for a letter.

1   Dad a _ _ _ _ _ _ _ the telephone when it rang.

2   Truth is stranger than f _ _ _ _ _ _.

3   Islam is the r _ _ _ _ _ _ _ of most Arabs.

4   Felix played a lively tune on his x _ _ _ _ _ _ _ _.

5   Americans refer to the a _ _ _ _ _ as the fall.

6   It's going to rain, a _ _ _ _ _ _ _ _ to the forecast.

7   Mr Skinner s _ _ _ _ _ his name on the letter.

8   Mr Patel built a thriving grocery b _ _ _ _ _ _ _.

9   Terry has a big c _ _ _ _ _ _ _ _ _ of coins.

10   These strawberries are absolutely d _ _ _ _ _ _ _ _.

11   Angus had an o _ _ _ _ _ _ _ _ on his broken leg.

12   To our a _ _ _ _ _ _ _ _ Kevin had washed up.

13   If the stamps are stuck together you must
     s _ _ _ _ _ _ _ them.

14   Concorde is a supersonic a _ _ _ _ _ _ _ _.

15   The gladiator looked at his o _ _ _ _ _ _ _ with
     contempt.

16   Oh dear, I s _ _ _ _ _ _ you all want to come.

17   P.C. Plodd hit Silas with his t _ _ _ _ _ _ _ _.

18   The residents have formed a c _ _ _ _ _ _ _ _ to run
     things.

19   The p _ _ _ _ _ _ _ _ _ of the world grows every
     minute.

20   You were very e _ _ _ _ _ _ _ _ _ _ to buy so many
     cakes.